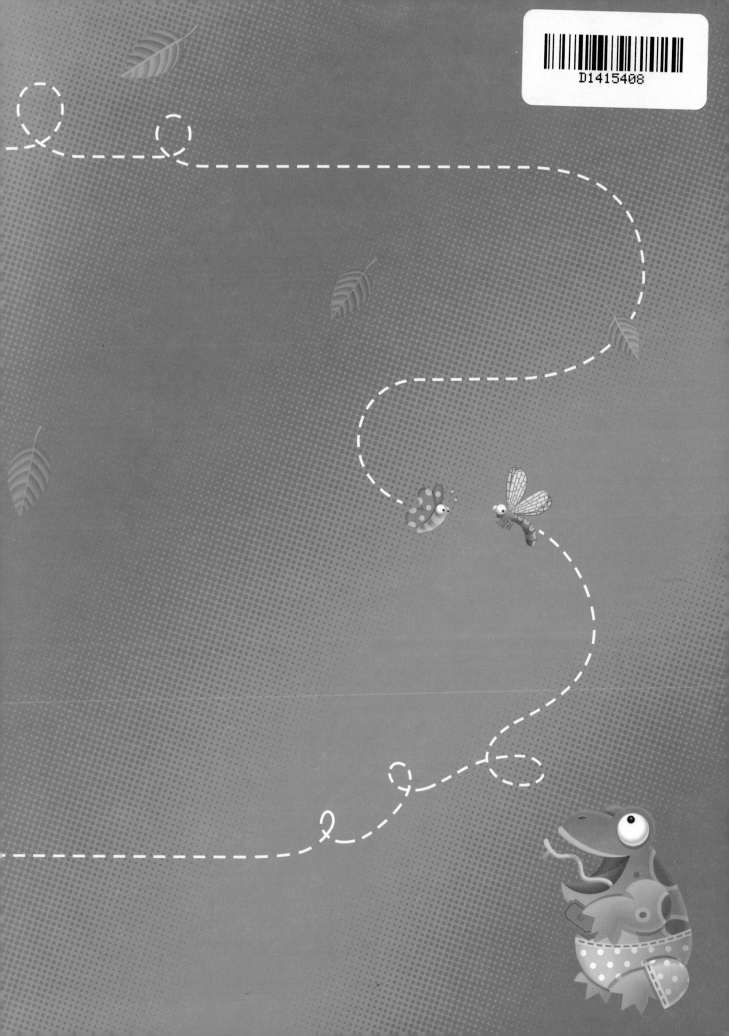

Cause and Effect

Details and Facts

Draw Conclusions

Steps in a Process

Literary Elements

PICTURE IT!

A Comprehension Handbook

Cause and Effect

Cause

Effect

Details and Facts

Draw Conclusions

= Sad

Steps in a Process

Literary Elements

Characters

BROTHER

MOMMY

DADDY

SISTER

Setting

Plot

Beginning

Middle

End

ISBN-13: 978-0-328-36588-3
ISBN-10:   0-328-36588-2

1 2 3 4 5 6 7 8 9 10 V063 17 16 15 14 13 12 11 10 09 08

Program Authors

Peter Afflerbach

Camille Blachowicz

Candy Dawson Boyd

Wendy Cheyney

Connie Juel

Edward Kame'enui

Donald Leu

Jeanne Paratore

Sam Sebesta

Deborah Simmons

Alfred Tatum

Sharon Vaughn

Susan Watts Taffe

Karen Kring Wixson

PEARSON

Glenview, Illinois • Boston, Massachusetts • Mesa, Arizona
Shoreview, Minnesota • Upper Saddle River, New Jersey

Unit 4 Contents

Treasures

 What do we treasure?

Surprising Treasures

Treasures to Share

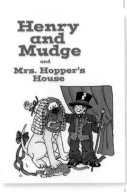

Picture It! A Comprehension Handbook **PI•1- PI•5**

Unit 4

Get Online!
PearsonSuccessNet.com

See It!
- Concept Talk Video
- Background Building Audio Slide Show
- Picture It! Animation
- e-Books

Hear It!
- Amazing Words Sing with Me
- Selection Snapshot and Response
- Paired Selection e-Text
- Grammar Jammer
- e-Books

Do It!
- Online Journal
- Story Sort
- New Literacies Activity
- Success Tracker

Treasures

 THE BIG **?** What do we treasure?

Let's Talk About
Surprising Treasures

LS1.1 Listen attentively. LS1.4 Stay on the topic when speaking.
LS1.5 Use descriptive words when speaking about people, places, things, and events.

Words to Read

give
surprise
would
enjoy
worry
about

R1.11 Read common, irregular sight words (e.g., *the, have, said, come, give, of*).

Read the Words

Francisco wants to give his mother a surprise party. Francisco thinks she would enjoy it. But he does worry that she will find out about the party. Can he surprise her?

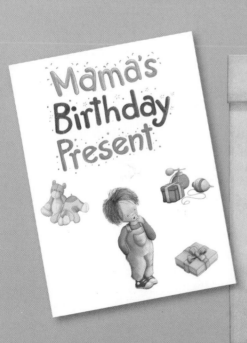

Mama's Birthday Present

Genre: Realistic Fiction
Realistic fiction is a made-up story that could really happen. Next you will read about a birthday surprise.

Mama's Birthday Present

by Carmen Tafolla

illustrated by Gabriel Pacheco

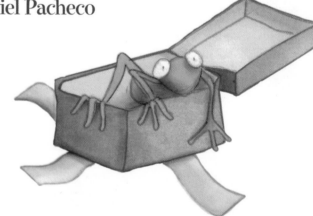

What is Mama's birthday present?

Francisco ran into the garden.
His grandmother was reading a book.

"Grandma! Grandma!" called Francisco.
"Next Sunday is Mama's birthday! Mama
always surprises me with a party for my
birthday. Can we surprise Mama with a party?"

"That is a wonderful idea, Francisco," said Grandma. "Today is Monday. If we begin today, we will have seven days to plan a party."

"Mama always gives me a present for my birthday," said Francisco. "What present can I give Mama?"

"I don't know," said Grandma. "But don't worry. We can make a piñata to break. Your mama will enjoy that."

So Grandma and Francisco made a piñata.

On Tuesday, Francisco wondered about Mama's present. Francisco went to talk with Papa about Mama's birthday party.

"What present can I give Mama?" asked Francisco.

"I don't know," said Papa. "But don't worry. I can play my guitar. Your mama will enjoy that."

So Papa promised Francisco he would play his guitar.

On Wednesday, Francisco wondered about Mama's present. Francisco and his older brother went to invite Señora Molina to Mama's party. Señora Molina had a tortilla shop.

"What present can I give Mama?" asked Francisco.

"I don't know," said Señora Molina. "But don't worry. I can bring some hot tortillas, fresh off the stove. Your mama will enjoy that."

So Señora Molina promised Francisco she would bring hot tortillas, fresh off the stove.

On Thursday, Francisco wondered about
Mama's present. He went to talk to his friend
Gina about it.

"What present can I give Mama?"
asked Francisco.

"I don't know," said Gina. "But don't worry. We can make confetti eggs to crack on people's heads. Your mama will enjoy that."

So Gina and Francisco filled and painted the bright confetti eggs.

On Friday, Francisco wondered about
Mama's present. So he went to speak to
Grandpa Pérez.

"What present can I give Mama?"
asked Francisco.

"I don't know," said Grandpa Pérez. "But don't worry. We can make some sweet buñuelos. Your mama will enjoy that."

So Francisco and Grandpa Pérez made some sweet buñuelos.

On Saturday, Francisco still wondered about his present for Mama. But Francisco had many things to do.

He helped his brothers
and sisters look for a place
to hang the piñata.

He talked to Papa
about the songs Papa
would play on his guitar.

He talked to Señora Molina
about the tortillas she would bring.

He found a
safe place to hide
Gina's confetti eggs

and Grandpa Pérez's
sweet buñuelos.

Everyone was ready for Mama's surprise.

On Sunday, everyone came to the party. Mama was very surprised.

Papa played his guitar. Señora Molina's hot tortillas smelled wonderful. Grandpa's sweet buñuelos tasted wonderful.

Everyone ate and sang and had fun. The children cracked confetti eggs over everyone's heads. Then they all lined up to take a swing at the piñata.

Everyone looked happy. Everyone except Francisco.

"Francisco, what is the matter?" asked Mama.

"I did not know what to give you for your birthday, Mama."

"Oh, Francisco," said Mama. "This party
was the best present you could give me. No,
the second best."

"Second best?" asked Francisco.

"Yes. The best present of all is having my family and friends here with me. That is the most wonderful part of a party!"

Mama gave Francisco a big hug. Then they all took turns hitting the piñata. The one who broke it was Francisco.

And Mama enjoyed that.

Talk About It "Don't worry," everyone says to Francisco. What advice would you have given him about what to give Mama?

1. Use the pictures below to retell the story. **Retell**

2. Why was a gift for Mama so important to Francisco? **Draw Conclusions**

3. Look at page 30. Read the words. How did you know what *tortillas* means? **Context Clues**

TEST PRACTICE

Look Back and Write Look back at pages 40–43. What is Mama's birthday present from Francisco?

Retell

R2.2 Respond to *who, what, when, where,* and *how* questions.
R2.4 Use context to resolve ambiguities about word and sentence meanings.

Meet the Author
Carmen Tafolla

Carmen Tafolla grew up in San Antonio, Texas. She tells stories and writes poems about her Mexican American neighborhood.

Dr. Tafolla works with schools around the world to help children of all races and languages to succeed. She lives in a 100-year-old house in San Antonio with her husband, son, mother, and lots of books.

Read more books about treasures.

Chinese Surprises

by Annie Brannan

Do you ever eat Chinese food? If so, then you may know about these Chinese desserts. Inside each one is a small note. The note's message sometimes gives advice.

If you take time to laugh, you would enjoy life more.

Don't worry. Work hard and good things will happen.

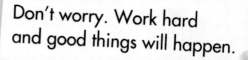

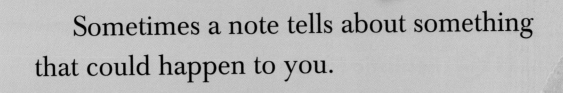

Sometimes a note tells about something that could happen to you.

Some day soon you will take a long trip.

Good things come to those who wait.

Why do people like these little desserts so much? People enjoy surprises!

Writing Realistic Fiction

Prompt In *Mama's Birthday Present*, a boy wants to surprise his mother on her birthday. Think about a surprise you would like to give as a gift. Now write a realistic story about it.

> **Writing Trait**
>
> Good **sentences** do not have too many extra words.

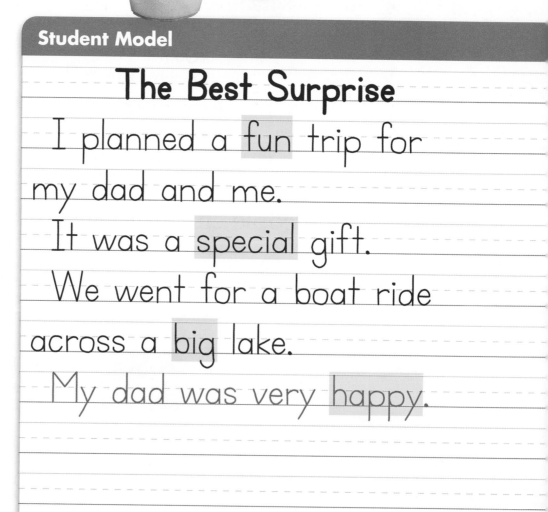

Student Model

The Best Surprise

I planned a fun trip for my dad and me.

It was a special gift.

We went for a boat ride across a big lake.

My dad was very happy.

Adjectives describe nouns.

A realistic story has events that could happen in real life.

Good sentences do not have extra words.

W1.2 Use descriptive words when writing. **W1.3** Print legibly and space letters, words, and sentences appropriately. **W2.1** Write brief narratives(e.g. fictional, autobiographical) describing an experience.

Grammar Adjectives

An **adjective** tells about a person, place, animal, or thing.

The **tall** man pats the **cute** puppy.
I saw a **red** rug at the **new** store.

Practice Look at the model. Write the adjectives. Then write what each adjective describes.

Let's Talk About
Surprising Treasures

LS1.1 Listen attentively. **LS1.4** Stay on the topic when speaking.
LS1.5 Use descriptive words when speaking about people, places, things, and events.

Words to Read

draw
colors
over
drew
great
sign
show

R1.11 Read common, irregular sight words (e.g., *the, have, said, come, give, of*).

Read the Words

In art class we draw with pencils. Then we mix colors and paint over the drawings. I drew a great big cat. Let me sign it. Then I will show it to you.

The Dot

Genre: Realistic Fiction

Realistic fiction stories are made up, but they have characters that seem real. In the next story you will see what happens to one small dot.

The Dot

by Peter H. Reynolds

How can a dot be a treasure?

Art class was over, but Vashti sat glued to her chair. Her paper was empty.

Vashti's teacher leaned over the blank paper.
"Ah! A polar bear in a snowstorm," she said.
"Very funny!" said Vashti. "I just CAN'T draw!"

Her teacher smiled. "Just
make a mark and see where it
takes you."

Vashti grabbed a marker and gave the
paper a good, strong jab. "There!"

Her teacher picked up the paper and studied it carefully. "Hmmmmm."

She pushed the paper toward Vashti and quietly said, "Now sign it."

Vashti thought for a moment.
"Well, maybe I can't draw, but I
CAN sign my name."

The next week, when Vashti walked into art class, she was surprised to see what was hanging above her teacher's desk.

It was the little dot she had drawn—HER DOT! All framed in swirly gold!

"Hmmph! I can make a
better dot than THAT!"

She opened her never-before-used
set of watercolors and set to work.
Vashti painted and painted.

A red dot.
A purple dot.
A yellow dot.
A blue dot.

The blue mixed with the yellow. She
discovered that she could make a GREEN dot.

Vashti kept experimenting.
Lots of little dots in many colors.

"If I can make little dots, I can make BIG dots too." Vashti splashed her colors with a bigger brush on bigger paper to make bigger dots.

Vashti even made a dot
by NOT painting a dot.

At the school art show a few weeks later,
Vashti's many dots made quite a splash.

Vashti noticed a little boy
gazing up at her.
"You're a really great artist.
I wish I could draw," he said.

"I bet you can," said Vashti.
"ME? No, not me. I can't draw
a straight line with a ruler."

Vashti smiled. She handed the boy a blank sheet of paper. "Show me."

The boy's pencil shook as he drew his line.

Vashti stared at the boy's squiggle.
And then she said . . .

"Sign it."

Talk About It Vashti didn't think she could draw. How did her teacher help her? Has anything like this happened to you? Explain.

1. Use the pictures below to retell the story. **Retell**

2. What lesson did Vashti learn from her teacher? **Draw Conclusions**

3. Look at page 66. Read the words. How does the picture help you understand what the words mean? **Monitor and Clarify**

Look Back and Write Look back at the selection. How can a dot be a treasure?

Retell

R2.2 Respond to *who, what, when, where,* and *how* questions.
R3.3 Recollect, talk, and write about books read during the school year.

Meet the Author and Illustrator

Peter H. Reynolds

Peter Reynolds says *The Dot* "is a book that encourages us to be brave about expressing ourselves. It gently reminds us to start small and explore the idea."

Mr. Reynolds collects ideas for stories in his journal. He likes to doodle on scraps of paper. He collects these little drawings in old tin boxes.

Read more books by Peter H. Reynolds.

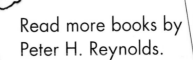

Meet José Ramírez

When José Ramírez was a boy, he liked to ride his bike. He liked to play baseball and video games. José also liked the paintings on walls in his city.

One day José visited his uncle in Mexico. He saw his Uncle Manuel draw plans for houses. From that day, José liked art. He started to draw.

Now José Ramírez is an artist and a teacher.
His art has lots of colors.

People see his art in stories, on walls,
and in paintings. Now you can see it too.

Read Together

Writing Realistic Fiction

Prompt *The Dot* tells how a girl creates art from dots. Think about another way an artist can create a treasure. Now write a realistic story about it.

Writing Trait

Put story events in order to show the **sequence.**

Student Model

A realistic story has events that could really happen.

Adjectives name shapes and colors.

The story events are in the correct order.

The Artist's Treasure

Dell made art from junk. One day he made a special work of art. First, he found his father's old blue shirts and white shirts. Next, he sewed them together. Dell made a square quilt. Then he gave it to his mother.

W1.2 Use descriptive words when writing. **W2.1** Write brief narratives (e.g., fictional, autobiographical) describing an experience. **LC1.6** Use knowledge of the basic rules of punctuation and capitalization when writing.

Grammar Adjectives for Colors and Shapes

Some **adjectives** name colors.
Some **adjectives** name shapes.

> Vashti draws a **blue** flower.
> She draws a **square** box.

Practice Look at the model. Find one adjective that names a color and one adjective that names a shape. Write the adjectives.

Let's Talk About

Surprising Treasures

LS1.1 Listen attentively. LS1.4 Stay on the topic when speaking.
LS1.5 Use descriptive words when speaking about people, places, things and events.

Words to Read

once
found
wild
took
mouth

R1.11 Read common, irregular sight words (e.g., *the, have, said, come, give, of*).

Read the Words

Once people found a big bird in the wild. Our country took this beautiful bird to stand for our land. Watch that bird catch a fish and put it in its mouth!

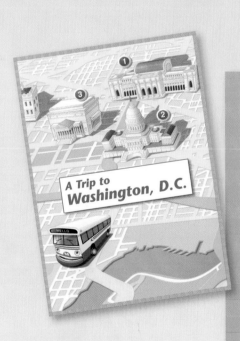

A Trip to Washington, D.C.

Genre: Expository Nonfiction

Expository nonfiction tells about real people, places, and events. Next you will read about Washington, D.C., the capital of our country.

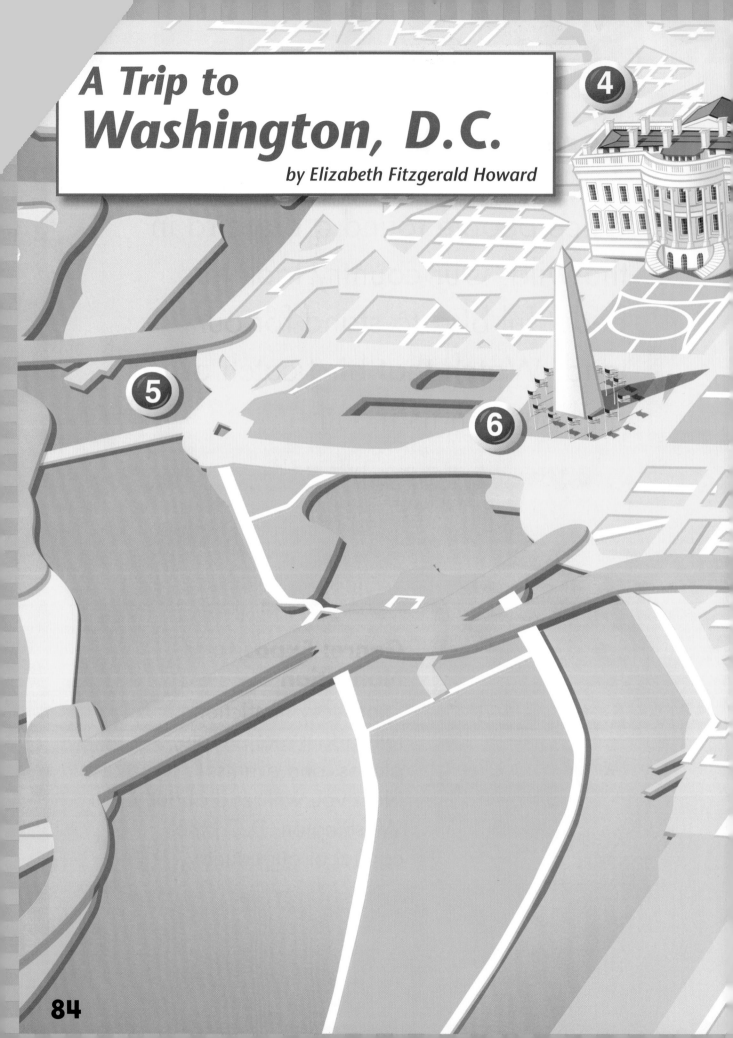

A Trip to
Washington, D.C.

by Elizabeth Fitzgerald Howard

What can you see in Washington, D.C.?

Hi! My name is Metro Mike, and I'm here to show you, Washington, D.C.! Every year people come to this city from all over. Do you know why? It is the capital of our country.

Come with me! I'll show you this splendid city. Sometimes I have a busload of people. But now this coach is just for you.

In Washington, D.C., the leaders of our country make laws. Laws are rules we follow. How do those people become our leaders? We vote for them. When people vote, they pick who will make the laws that we all follow.

Our first stop is on your right. That's the home of two documents. One is the Declaration of Independence. That paper says that Americans have the right to be free. The other is the U.S. Constitution. It is a plan for our government.

Declaration of Independence

Constitution

Washington, D.C., was named after George Washington, our first President. The President is the leader of our country. Many people call George Washington the "Father of Our Country."

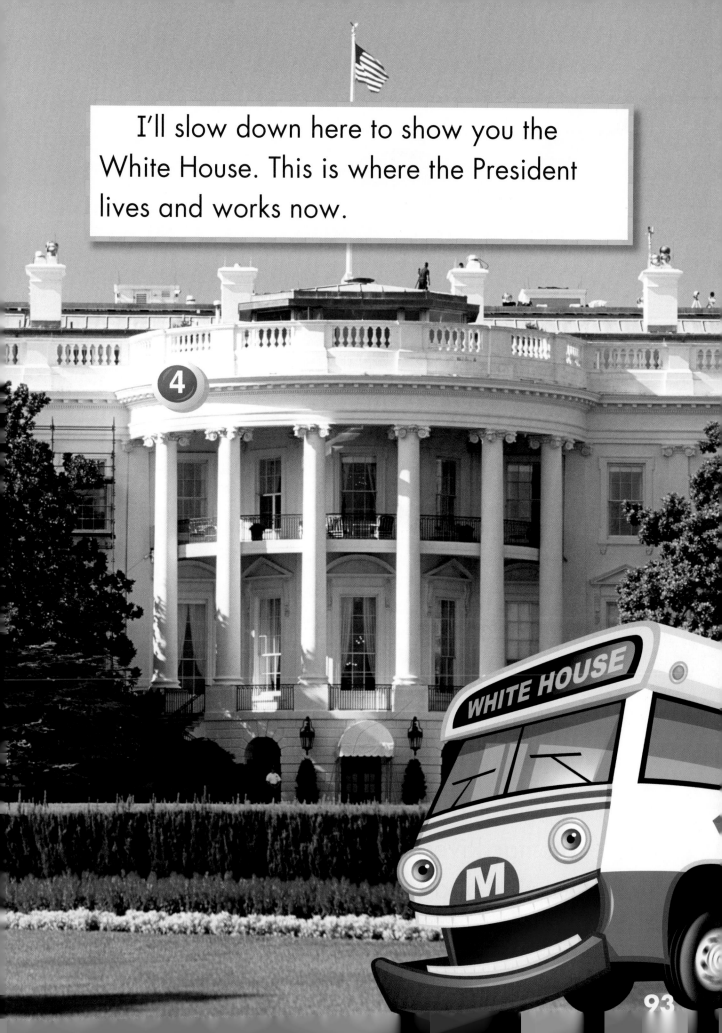

I'll slow down here to show you the White House. This is where the President lives and works now.

5

This next road will take us by the Potomac River. Look up in the sky! That beautiful bird stands for America. It is strong and free!

Did you see that splash? That bird took a fish to put in its mouth. Once there weren't many of these birds in the wild. Now there are many more.

Down that street you'll see lots of flags! In Washington, D.C., you will see the Stars and Stripes flying in many places. This red, white, and blue flag also stands for America.

6

Here we are, back at the start. I hope you found Washington, D.C., to be a great city. Come back again soon!

GOOD-BYE

Talk About It The author wrote *A Trip to Washington, D.C.* to tell about the capital of our country. Why is our capital an important place?

1. Use the pictures below to summarize what you learned. Summarize

2. Who was our capital named after? Why? Details and Facts

3. Look back at the numbers on the map on pages 84–85. How did the numbers help you as you read the rest of the selection? Monitor and Clarify

TEST PRACTICE

Look Back and Write Look back at the selection. What can we see in Washington, D.C.?

Summarize

R2.7 Retell the central ideas of simple expository or narrative passages.
R3.3 Recollect, talk, and write about books read during the school year.

Meet the Author

Elizabeth Fitzgerald Howard

When she is not writing about important places such as Washington, D.C., Elizabeth Fitzgerald Howard often writes stories based on people in her family. Her father told her many stories about his family and childhood while she was growing up. After she retired from teaching, Ms. Howard turned several family stories into children's books.

Read more books by Elizabeth Fitzgerald Howard.

Famous Places In America

by Penny Dowdy

The Golden Gate Bridge is in California. Many people drive on this beautiful landmark. Some ride their bikes or walk on it. Boats below look tiny to them.

Mount Rushmore is in South Dakota. You can see the faces of four American Presidents on it. Did you know? Each face is about as tall as 10 people!

George Washington

Thomas Jefferson

Theodore Roosevelt

Abraham Lincoln

Writing Expository Description

Prompt In *A Trip to Washington, D.C.*, readers learn about treasures on a field trip to the nation's capital. Think about a field trip you would like to take. Write a description of treasures you might see.

Writing Trait

Focus your writing on one clear main idea.

Writing focuses on one clear main idea.

Description helps readers create a picture in their minds.

Adjectives can describe size.

Student Model

My Field Trip

I'd take a trip to the biggest zoo in the world. Huge animals would live there. Tiny animals would live there too. The big tigers might be scary. But the little monkeys would be fun.

W1.1 Select a focus when writing. W1.2 Use descriptive words when writing.
L1.1 Write and speak in complete, coherent sentences.

Grammar Adjectives for Sizes

Some **adjectives** describe size. Words such as **big, small, long,** and **short** describe size.

That is a **big** flag.

Practice Look at the model. Find three adjectives that describe size. Write the adjectives.

Let's Talk About
Treasures
to Share

LS1.1 Listen attentively. **LS1.4** Stay on the topic when speaking.
LS1.5 Use descriptive words when speaking about people, places, things and events.

Words to Read

eight
moon
above
touch
laugh

R1.11 Read common, irregular sight words (e.g., *the, have, said, come, give, of*).

Read the Words

All eight of us looked at the moon above us. It looked close enough to touch. This night was going to be fun. We began to laugh.

The Lady in the Moon

Genre: Realistic Fiction
Realistic fiction stories are made-up stories, but they tell about events that seem real. Next you will read about a special celebration.

The Lady in the Moon

by Lily Wong Fillmore
illustrated by Lin Wang

Who is the Lady in the Moon?

The sun sets. The moon rises.
Come out. Come out to play.
It is Moon Festival, a night
for children everywhere.

Let's sing a song to the Lady in the Moon.
Let's write a poem to send to Lady Moon.

We'll make some treats, good things to eat. We'll wrap them in lotus leaves, tied with golden knots.

Moon cakes,
golden pears,
melons, and plums.

We'll make eight treasures rice, wrapped in lotus leaves.

Night is falling, and children call,

"Come out, Lady Moon.
Come light up the sky."

High above the city, high above the hills, the moon shows her golden face. Children sing and laugh. They send their poems to the Lady in the Moon.

She glows, she glides, she grows.
Lady Moon fills the sky with light.
Let's laugh and sing a song to Lady Moon.
Let's read our poems to Lady Moon.

We'll make her some treats,
good things to eat. We'll
wrap them in lotus leaves,
tied with golden knots.

Moon cakes,
golden pears,
melons, plums, and
eight treasures rice.

117

Raise your lanterns high. It is Moon Festival, a night for children everywhere. The moon is so near, you can touch it if you try. We light our lanterns. We raise them high.

Moon beams and
lanterns touch.
Oh, what a show!

A bridge of light glows
in the fall night.

Where does it go?
Will it take us to the moon?

Let's laugh and sing a song to Lady Moon.
Let's read our poems to the Lady in the Moon.
We'll take her some treats, good things to eat.

We'll wrap them
in lotus leaves,
tied with golden knots.

Moon cakes,
golden pears,
melons, plums, and
eight treasures rice.

Talk About It What part of the Moon Festival would be your favorite? Tell why.

1. Use the pictures below to retell the important parts of *The Lady in the Moon.* Retell

2. What are three things that happen during the Moon Festival? Describe them. Details and Facts

3. What did you wonder about as you read this story? What did you do to find out more? Monitor and Clarify

Look Back and Write Who is the Lady in the Moon? Look back at pages 114–116.

Retell

R2.2 Respond to *who, what, when, where,* and *how* questions. R3.3 Recollect, talk, and write about books read during the school year.

Meet the Author

Lily Wong Fillmore

As a child, Lily Wong Fillmore loved the Moon Festival. It was a time to eat fruits and moon cakes. It was a time to stay up late and have fun.

"If clouds got near the moon, we children were told to make a lot of noise," says Ms. Fillmore. "No one wanted clouds to cover the moon. It was the one night of the year we could play outdoors and make as much noise as we pleased."

Read more books about Asian celebrations.

My 4th of July

My family has fun on the 4th of July. Mom bakes eight pies to share at the block party.

We wrap red, white, and blue ribbons on our bikes.

We laugh as we try to win the sack race.

Dad knows the best place to watch the fireworks at night. Crack! Bang! They light up the sky above us.

Will the fireworks touch the moon? We laugh and cheer. What a beautiful sight!

Read Together

Writing Realistic Fiction

Prompt In *The Lady in the Moon*, children enjoy a special day. Think about a holiday you enjoy. Now write a realistic story about something that happens on that day.

Writing Trait

Your **voice** shows how you feel about a topic.

Student Model

A Special Holiday

Valentine's Day is a special day.

Last year I made pink cards with lace hearts.

My best friend made the same kind.

Then we gave one to each other.

It was so funny!

Adjectives can tell what kind.

A realistic story has events that could happen in real life.

Voice shows how you feel about your topic.

W1.2 Use descriptive words when writing. **W2.1** Write brief narratives (e.g., fictional, autobiographical) describing an experience.

Writer's Checklist

✓ Does my story have events that could really happen?

✓ Do I show how I feel about my topic?

✓ Do I use adjectives to tell what kind?

Grammar Adjectives for What Kind

An **adjective** can tell what kind.

Happy children picked **ripe** berries.

Happy tells what kind of children.
Ripe tells what kind of berries.

Practice Look at the story about Valentine's Day. Write the adjectives that tell what kind of day, what kind of hearts, and what kind of friend.

Let's Talk About
Treasures to Share

LS1.1 Listen attentively. **LS1.4** Stay on the topic when speaking.
LS1.5 Use descriptive words when speaking about people, places, things and events.

Words to Read

stood
room
thought
picture
remember

R1.11 Read common, irregular sight words (e.g., *the, have, said, come, give, of*).

Read the Words

Peter stood in his room. He thought he would take down his baby picture. Did anyone remember when he was a baby?

Genre: Realistic Fiction
Realistic fiction has make-believe characters who act like real people. Next you will read about a boy who has a new baby sister.

PETER'S
CHAIR

by Ezra Jack Keats

What is special about Peter's chair?

Peter stretched as high as he could.
There! His tall building was finished.

CRASH! Down it came.

"Shhhh!" called his mother. "You'll have to play more quietly. Remember, we have a new baby in the house."

Peter looked into his sister Susie's room. His mother was fussing around the cradle.

"That's my cradle," he thought, "and they painted it pink!"

"Hi, Peter," said his father. "Would you like to help paint Sister's high chair?"
"It's my high chair," whispered Peter.

He saw his crib and muttered, "My crib. It's painted pink too."

Not far away stood his old chair.

"They didn't paint that yet!" Peter shouted.

He picked it up and ran to his room.

"Let's run away, Willie," he said. Peter filled
a shopping bag with cookies and dog biscuits.

"We'll take my blue chair, my toy crocodile,
and the picture of me when I was a baby."

Willie got his bone.

They went outside and stood in front of his house.

"This is a good place," said Peter. He arranged his things very nicely and decided to sit in his chair for a while.

But he couldn't fit in
the chair. He was too big!

His mother came to the window and called, "Won't you come back to us, Peter dear? We have something very special for lunch."

Peter and Willie made believe they didn't hear. But Peter got an idea.

Soon his mother saw signs that Peter was home. "That rascal is hiding behind the curtain," she said happily.

Peter sat in a grown-up chair.
His father sat next to him.

"Daddy," said Peter, "let's paint the little chair pink for Susie."

154

And they did.

Talk About It Did you understand why Peter was sad? Have you ever felt as Peter did?

1. Use the pictures below to retell the story. Retell

2. Who are the characters in the story? Where does the story take place? What is the story about? Character, Setting, and Plot

3. What questions did you ask yourself as you read? Ask Questions

Look Back and Write What is special about Peter's chair? Look back at pages 140–143.

Retell

R2.7 Retell the central ideas of simple expository or narrative passages.
R3.1 Identify and describe the elements of plot, setting, and characters in a story, as well as the story's beginning, middle, and end.

Meet the Author and Illustrator
Ezra Jack Keats

Ezra Jack Keats was an artist and author. He grew up in Brooklyn, New York, and often wrote about city life.

His first story about Peter, *The Snowy Day,* won the Caldecott Medal and made him famous. Mr. Keats died in 1983.

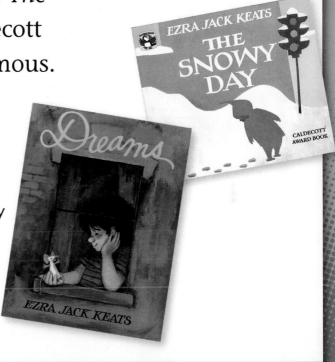

Read more books by Ezra Jack Keats.

Read Together

Peter's Baby Sister

Peter lives far from his grandmother.
They share news by e-mail. See how.
1. Peter types his e-mail.

| Write | Reply | Send | Forward | Delete | Address | Print |

Hi, Grandma!

I have a new little sister.
Did you have a little sister?
What was it like?
Please come to see us.

Peter

2. Then Peter clicks his mouse on the SEND button. In a flash, Grandma gets Peter's e-mail.

3. Grandma reads Peter's e-mail.

4. Then she writes back.

Write   Reply   Send   Forward   Delete   Address   Print

Dear Peter,

I had a little sister too. I helped care for her. Many things have changed since then.
I will visit next month.

Grandma

Read Together

Writing Realistic Fiction

Prompt In *Peter's Chair*, a boy finds something to share with his new baby sister. Think about something children sometimes share with their siblings. Now write a realistic story about brothers or sisters sharing.

Writing Trait

Capital letters, punctuation, and spelling are **conventions** that help readers understand your writing.

Student Model

A realistic story has events that could really happen.

Adjectives can tell how many.

Sentences start with capital letters and end with periods.

A Ball to Share

Sally and Billy wanted to play with the new ball. But there was only one ball. The two kids played together. First Sally tossed the ball to Billy. Then Billy tossed the ball to Sally.

W1.2 Use descriptive words when writing. **W2.1** Write brief narratives (e.g., fictional, autobiographical) describing an experience. **LC1.6** Use knowledge of the basic rules of punctuation and capitalization when writing.

Grammar Adjectives for How Many

Some **adjectives** tell how many.

Peter packed **five** cookies and **three** dog biscuits.

. . . .

Practice Look at the model. Write the adjectives that tell how many.

Let's Talk About
Treasures to Share

LS1.1 Listen attentively. **LS1.4** Stay on the topic when speaking.
LS1.5 Use descriptive words when speaking about people, places, things and events.

Words to Read

told
only
across
because
dance
opened
shoes

R1.11 Read common, irregular sight words (e.g., *the, have, said, come, give, of*).

Read the Words

Henry told Mudge they were only going across the street to Mrs. Hopper's house. They were staying with Mrs. Hopper because Mom and Dad were going to a dance. Mrs. Hopper opened the door. Henry walked in and took off his shoes.

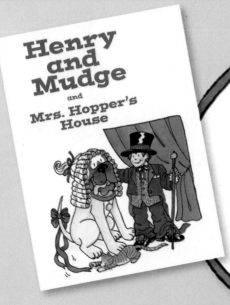

Genre: Realistic Fiction
Realistic fiction has settings that seem real, but the stories are made up. Next you will find out what happens when Henry and Mudge visit a neighbor.

Henry and Mudge

and

Mrs. Hopper's House

by Cynthia Rylant

illustrated by Carolyn Bracken
in the style of Suçie Stevenson

What will Henry and Mudge find at Mrs. Hopper's house?

A Sweetheart Dance

Valentine's Day was coming. Henry and his big dog Mudge loved Valentine's Day because of the candy. They liked the candy hearts that said "You're swell" and "Oh, dear" and things like that.

Henry read the words, and Mudge licked
them off. They were a good team.

On this Valentine's Day Henry's father and Henry's mother were going to a Sweetheart Dance. Henry and Mudge would be staying with Mrs. Hopper.

Mrs. Hopper lived across the street in a big stone house with droopy trees and dark windows and a gargoyle on the door.

Henry liked Mrs. Hopper. But he did not like her house.

"Are you sure Mudge and I can't come to the Sweetheart Dance?" Henry asked his father.

"Only if you both promise to wear a
tuxedo and shiny black shoes and waltz to
'The Blue Danube,'" said Henry's father.

Henry looked at Mudge and tried to imagine him in a tuxedo and shiny black shoes, waltzing to "The Blue Danube."

"I think we'd better go to Mrs. Hopper's," Henry said.

"Good idea," said Henry's father.

"Because Mudge only knows how to tap-dance," Henry said with a grin.

Costumes

Mrs. Hopper wasn't like anyone Henry
had ever met. She played the violin for him.
She served him tea. She told him about her
father, who had been a famous actor.

She was very kind to Mudge. She cooked him a bowl of oatmeal and gave him his own loaf of French bread.

After the tea and music and oatmeal, Mrs. Hopper took them upstairs. She opened a room that had been her father's.

"Wow!" said Henry. The room was full
of costumes.

There were silk capes and tall hats and shiny coats. There were canes and swords and umbrellas. There were wigs.

Mrs. Hopper put a wig on Mudge.
"You look like a poodle, Mudge!"
said Henry.
Mudge wagged and wagged.

Henry and Mudge and Mrs. Hopper spent most of the evening in the costume room. They had a wonderful time.

And when Henry's parents came back from the dance, were they ever surprised. Mudge was a poodle, and Henry was a man! Henry wore a tuxedo and a hat and shiny black shoes.

"I bet you didn't know I was this handsome," Henry told his dad. And everyone laughed and laughed.

Read
Together

Talk About It Who do you think had a better time on Valentine's Day, Henry or his parents? Tell why you think as you do.

1. Use the pictures below to retell the story. Retell

2. Why did Mrs. Hopper have so many costumes? Cause and Effect

3. Look at pages 174–175. Read the words. How did you know what *waltz* means? Context Clues

TEST PRACTICE **Look Back and Write** Look back at pages 179–181. What do Henry and Mudge find at Mrs. Hopper's house?

Retell

R2.4 Use context to resolve ambiguities about word and sentence meanings.
R2.2 Respond to *who, what, when, where,* and *how* questions.

Meet the Author
Cynthia Rylant

Cynthia Rylant grew up in West Virginia. She says, "I lived in a place called Cool Ridge, in a four-room house with my grandparents. We had no running water and my grandparents grew and hunted most of our food."

Ms. Rylant has written many books about Henry and Mudge. Now she lives in Oregon with her dogs Martha Jane and Gracie Rose.

Read more Henry and Mudge books.

Read Together

Good Books, Good Times!

by Lee Bennett Hopkins
illustrated by Luciana Navarro Alves

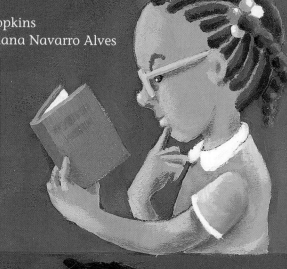

Good books.
Good times.
Good stories.
Good rhymes.
Good beginnings.
Good ends.
Good people.
Good friends.
Good fiction.
Good facts.
Good adventures.
Good acts.
Good stories.
Good rhymes.
Good books.
Good times.

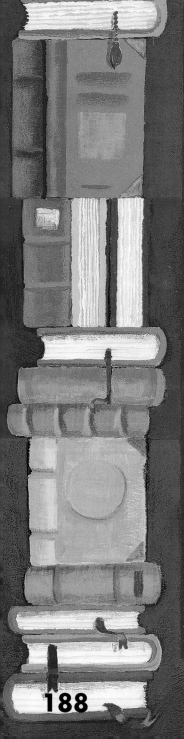

188

Dress-Up

by Bobbi Katz
illustrated by Luciana Navarro Alves

A treasure chest of castoff clothes!
    What's more fun, do you suppose?
With dandy costumes such as these
    we can dress up as we please!
A tie, a hat, a string of beads—
    are just the things that each kid needs!
Be a hunter or an elf—
    be *anyone* . . . except yourself!

Shell

by Myra Cohn Livingston
illustrated by Luciana Navarro Alves

When it was time
for Show and Tell,
Adam brought a big pink shell.

He told about
the ocean roar
and walking on the sandy shore.

And then he passed
the shell around.
We listened to the water sound.

And that's the first time
I could hear
the wild waves calling to my ear.

Reading

by Marchette Chute
illustrated by Luciana Navarro Alves

A story is a special thing.
　　The ones that I have read,
They do not stay inside the book,
　　They stay inside my head.

The Rainbow

by Iain Crichton Smith
illustrated by Luciana Navarro Alves

The rainbow's like a colored bridge
that sometimes shines from ridge to ridge.
Today one end is in the sea,
the other's in the field with me.

Writing Realistic Fiction

Prompt In *Henry and Mudge and Mrs. Hopper's House*, Mrs. Hopper shares treasures with Henry and Mudge. Think about a surprise treasure that might be in a neighbor's house. Now write a realistic story about it.

Writing Trait

Choose words that are interesting and give details.

Student Model

A realistic story tells about problems that real people could have.

Some adjectives compare.

The writer chooses words that give details.

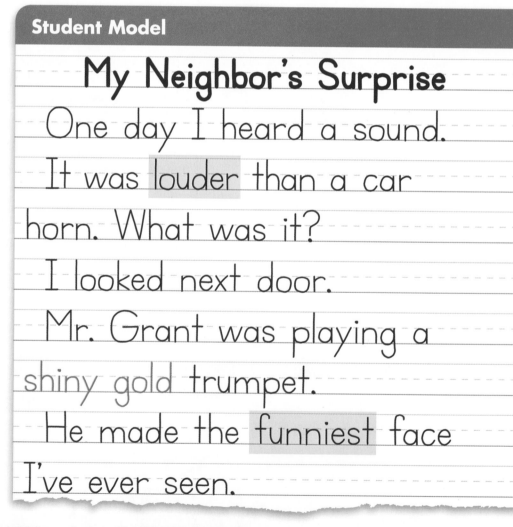

My Neighbor's Surprise

One day I heard a sound.

It was louder than a car

horn. What was it?

I looked next door.

Mr. Grant was playing a

shiny gold trumpet.

He made the funniest face

I've ever seen.

W1.2 Use descriptive words when writing. **W2.1** Write brief narratives (e.g., fictional, autobiographical) describing an experience. **LC1.5** Use a period, exclamation point, or question mark at the end of sentences.

Writer's Checklist

☑ Is my story about a problem that real people could have?

☑ Do I use words that are interesting and give details?

☑ Do I use adjectives that compare?

Grammar Adjectives That Compare

Add **-er** to an adjective to compare two persons, places, animals, or things. Add **-est** to an adjective to compare three or more persons, places, animals, or things.

That dog is **faster** than Mudge.
Mudge is the **slowest** dog of all.

Practice Look at the model. Write the adjectives that compare.

artist • capital

Aa

artist An **artist** is a person who makes art. **Artists** can make pictures and statues.

artist

Bb

biscuits **Biscuits** are small cakes that are not sweet.

break To **break** something means to make it come apart into pieces. If I drop a plate, it might **break**.

buñuelos **Buñuelos** are sweet pastries that are fried and then covered with sugar. **Buñuelos** are like doughnuts, but smaller.

Cc

capital The **capital** of a country is the city where the government is located. The **capital** of the United States is Washington, D.C.

confetti **Confetti** is bits of colored paper thrown during celebrations. We threw **confetti** at the birthday party.

cookies **Cookies** are small, flat, sweet cakes.

country A **country** is a land of a group of people who have the same government. The United States is a **country** in North America.

cradle A **cradle** is a small bed for a baby, usually one that can rock from side to side.

crocodile A **crocodile** is a large animal with thick skin, four short legs, and a pointed nose. **Crocodiles** look a lot like alligators.

crocodile

curtain A **curtain** is a cloth or other material hung across a window. **Curtains** are often used to keep out light.

Dd

document A **document** is something written or printed that gives information. Letters, maps, and pictures are **documents.**

Ee

experimenting When you are **experimenting,** you are testing or trying something out. The cook is **experimenting** with new recipes.

Ff

festival A **festival** is a special celebration. Some **festivals** include a parade.

festival

Gg

gargoyle A **gargoyle** is a decoration. It usually is made of stone and shaped like a scary animal or person. **Gargoyles** often decorate buildings.

gargoyle

glued If two things are **glued** together, it means they are stuck together.

gold **Gold** is a bright yellow metal that is worth a lot of money. **Gold** is used to make jewelry and some coins.

government A **government** is a group of people who manage a country. Our **government** includes the President, the Congress, and the Supreme Court.

guitar

guitar A **guitar** is a musical instrument that usually has six strings. You play a **guitar** with your fingers.

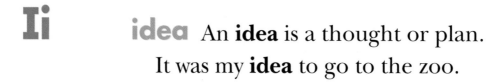

heart

Hh

heart A **heart** is a figure shaped like this. The card was covered with **hearts**.

Ii

idea An **idea** is a thought or plan. It was my **idea** to go to the zoo.

Ll

lotus leaves **Leaves** are the flat, green parts of a tree or plant. A **lotus** is a water plant that has **leaves** and flowers.

Pp

pears **Pears** are sweet fruits that are round at one end. **Pears** are green or yellow and grow on trees.

pears

piñata A **piñata** is a decorated pottery pot filled with candy, fruit, and small toys. Blindfolded children swing sticks in order to break the **piñata** and get what is inside.

piñata

poem A **poem** is like a song without music. **Poems** often use words that rhyme. **Poems** sometimes put words together to tell about feelings and thoughts.

present

present A **present** is a gift. A **present** is something that someone gives you or that you give someone. His uncle sent him a birthday **present.**

Ss

shiny Something that is **shiny** is bright. Mom gave me a **shiny** new penny.

splash If you **splash** water or some other liquid, you cause it to fly around.

splash

squiggle

squiggle A **squiggle** is a wiggly twist or curve. The child drew a **squiggle** on the paper.

Glossary

stared If you **stared,** you looked at someone with your eyes wide open for a long time. I **stared** at my sister.

straight If something is **straight,** it does not have a bend, turn, or curve. She drew a **straight** line. Try to stand up **straight.**

Tt

tortilla A **tortilla** is a thin, flat, round bread made of cornmeal. **Tortillas** are baked on a flat surface, and can be filled with rice, meat, beans, and other foods.

treasures **Treasures** are things that are worth a lot. The pirates drew a map to show where the **treasures** were buried.

tuxedo A **tuxedo** is a formal suit for boys and men. **Tuxedos** are usually black.

tuxedo

Vv   **Valentine's Day** **Valentine's Day** is February 14, a day when people send cards with hearts and small presents.

Ww   **waltz** To **waltz** means to dance slowly with graceful steps. Mom and Dad like to **waltz** together.

wonderful If something is **wonderful**, you like it very much. The ocean was a **wonderful** sight. She had a **wonderful** time at the party.

waltz

Mama's Birthday Present

about
enjoy
gives
surprise
worry
would

The Dot

colors
draw
drew
great
over
show
sign

A Trip to Washington, D.C.

found
mouth
once
took
wild

The Lady in the Moon

above
eight
laugh
moon
touch

Peter's Chair

picture
remember
room
stood
thought

Henry and Mudge and Mrs. Hopper's House

across
because
dance
only
opened
shoes
told

Reading

1.0 Word Analysis, Fluency, and Systematic Vocabulary Development

Students understand the basic features of reading. They select letter patterns and know how to translate them into spoken language by using phonics, syllabication, and word parts. They apply this knowledge to achieve fluent oral and silent reading.

Concepts About Print

1.1 Match oral words to printed words.
1.2 Identify the title and author of a reading selection.
1.3 Identify letters, words, and sentences.

Phonemic Awareness

1.4 Distinguish initial, medial, and final sounds in single-syllable words.
1.5 Distinguish long- and short-vowel sounds in orally stated single-syllable words (e.g., *bit/bite*).
1.6 Create and state a series of rhyming words, including consonant blends.
1.7 Add, delete, or change target sounds to change words (e.g., change *cow* to *how; pan* to *an*).
1.8 Blend two to four phonemes into recognizable words (e.g., /c/ a/ t/ = cat; /f/ l/ a/ t/ = flat).
1.9 Segment single-syllable words into their components (e.g., /c/ a/ t/ = cat; /s/ p/ l/ a/ t/ = splat; /r/ i/ ch/ = rich).

Decoding and Word Recognition

1.10 Generate the sounds from all the letters and letter patterns, including consonant blends and long- and short-vowel patterns (i.e., phonograms), and blend those sounds into recognizable words.
1.11 Read common, irregular sight words (e.g., *the, have, said, come, give, of*).
1.12 Use knowledge of vowel digraphs and *r-* controlled letter-sound associations to read words.
1.13 Read compound words and contractions.
1.14 Read inflectional forms (e.g., *-s, -ed, -ing*) and root words (e.g., *look, looked, looking*).
1.15 Read common word families (e.g., *-ite, -ate*).
1.16 Read aloud with fluency in a manner that sounds like natural speech.

Vocabulary and Concept Development

1.17 Classify grade-appropriate categories of words (e.g., concrete collections of animals, foods, toys).

2.0 Reading Comprehension

Students read and understand grade-level-appropriate material. They draw upon a variety of comprehension strategies as needed (e.g., generating and responding to essential questions, making predictions, comparing information from several sources). The selections in *Recommended Literature, Kindergarten Through Grade Twelve* illustrate the quality and complexity of the materials to be read by students. In addition to their regular school reading, by grade four, students read one-half million words annually, including a good representation of grade-level-appropriate narrative and expository text (e.g., classic and contemporary literature, magazines, newspapers, online information). In grade one, students begin to make progress toward this goal.

Structural Features of Informational Materials

2.1 Identify text that uses sequence or other logical order.

Comprehension and Analysis of Grade-Level-Appropriate Text

2.2 Respond to *who, what, when, where,* and *how* questions.
2.3 Follow one-step written instructions.
2.4 Use context to resolve ambiguities about word and sentence meanings.
2.5 Confirm predictions about what will happen next in a text by identifying key words (i.e., signpost words).
2.6 Relate prior knowledge to textual information.
2.7 Retell the central ideas of simple expository or narrative passages.

3.0 Literary Response and Analysis

Students read and respond to a wide variety of significant works of children's literature. They distinguish between the structural features of the text and the literary terms or elements (e.g., theme, plot, setting, characters). The selections in *Recommended Literature, Kindergarten Through Grade Twelve* illustrate the quality and complexity of the materials to be read by students.

Narrative Analysis of Grade-Level-Appropriate Text

3.1 Identify and describe the elements of plot, setting, and character(s) in a story, as well as the story's beginning, middle, and ending.
3.2 Describe the roles of authors and illustrators and their contributions to print materials.
3.3 Recollect, talk, and write about books read during the school year.

Writing

1.0 Writing Strategies
Students write clear and coherent sentences and paragraphs that develop a central idea. Their writing shows they consider the audience and purpose. Students progress through the stages of the writing process (e.g., prewriting, drafting, revising, editing successive versions).

Organization and Focus
1.1 Select a focus when writing.
1.2 Use descriptive words when writing.

Penmanship
1.3 Print legibly and space letters, words, and sentences appropriately.

2.0 Writing Applications (Genres and Their Characteristics)
Students write compositions that describe and explain familiar objects, events, and experiences. Student writing demonstrates a command of standard American English and the drafting, research, and organizational strategies outlined in Writing Standard 1.0.

Using the writing strategies of grade one outlined in Writing Standard 1.0, students:
2.1 Write brief narratives (e.g., fictional, autobiographical) describing an experience.
2.2 Write brief expository descriptions of a real object, person, place, or event, using sensory details.

Written and Oral English Language Conventions

The standards for written and oral English language conventions have been placed between those for writing and for listening and speaking because these conventions are essential to both sets of skills.

1.0 Written and Oral English Language Conventions
Students write and speak with a command of standard English conventions appropriate to this grade level.

Sentence Structure
1.1 Write and speak in complete, coherent sentences.

Grammar
1.2 Identify and correctly use singular and plural nouns.
1.3 Identify and correctly use contractions (e.g., *isn't, aren't, can't, won't*) and singular possessive pronouns (e.g., *my/ mine, his/ her, hers, your/s*) in writing and speaking.

Punctuation
1.4 Distinguish between declarative, exclamatory, and interrogative sentences.
1.5 Use a period, exclamation point, or question mark at the end of sentences.
1.6 Use knowledge of the basic rules of punctuation and capitalization when writing.

Capitalization
1.7 Capitalize the first word of a sentence, names of people, and the pronoun *I.*

Spelling
1.8 Spell three- and four-letter short-vowel words and grade-level-appropriate sight words correctly.

Listening and Speaking

1.0 Listening and Speaking Strategies
Students listen critically and respond appropriately to oral communication. They speak in a manner that guides the listener to understand important ideas by using proper phrasing, pitch, and modulation.

Comprehension
1.1 Listen attentively.
1.2 Ask questions for clarification and understanding.
1.3 Give, restate, and follow simple two-step directions.

Organization and Delivery of Oral Communication
1.4 Stay on the topic when speaking.
1.5 Use descriptive words when speaking about people, places, things, and events.

2.0 Speaking Applications (Genres and Their Characteristics)
Students deliver brief recitations and oral presentations about familiar experiences or interests that are organized around a coherent thesis statement. Student speaking demonstrates a command of standard American English and the organizational and delivery strategies outlined in Listening and Speaking Standard 1.0.

Using the speaking strategies of grade one outlined in Listening and Speaking Standard 1.0, students:
2.1 Recite poems, rhymes, songs, and stories.
2.2 Retell stories using basic story grammar and relating the sequence of story events by answering *who, what, when, where, why,* and *how* questions.
2.3 Relate an important life event or personal experience in a simple sequence.
2.4 Provide descriptions with careful attention to sensory detail.

Acknowledgments

Text

Page 20: "Mama's Birthday Present" by Dr. Carmen Tafolla, 1991. Reprinted by permission of Dr. Carmen Tafolla.

Page 54: *The Dot.* Copyright © 2003 by Peter H. Reynolds. Reproduced by permission of the publisher, Candlewick Press, Inc., Cambridge, MA.

Page 136: *Peter's Chair* by Ezra Jack Keats, 1967. © Ezra Jack Keats Foundation. Reprinted by permission.

Page 166: Reprinted with the permission of Simon & Schuster Books for Young Readers, an imprint of Simon & Schuster Children's Publishing Division from *Henry and Mudge and Mrs. Hopper's House* by Cynthia Rylant, illustrated by Carolyn Bracken in the style of Sucie Stevenson. Text copyright © 2003 Cynthia Rylant. Illustrations, Copyright © 2003 by Sucie Stevenson. All rights reserved.

Page 188: "Dress-Up" from *Poems for Small Friends* by Bobbi Katz, copyright © 1989 by Random House, Inc. Illustrations © 1989 by Gyo Fujikawa. Used by permission of Random House Children's Books, a division of Random House, Inc.

Page 188: "Good Books, Good Times!" from *Good Rhymes, Good Times* by Lee Bennett Hopkins. Copyright © 1995 by Lee Bennett Hopkins. First appeared in *Good Rhymes, Good Times* published by HarperCollins Publishers. Reprinted by permission of Curtis Brown, Ltd.

Page 190: "Shell" from *World's I Know and Other Poems* by Myra Cohn Livingston. Copyright © 1985 by Myra Cohn Livingston. Used by permission of Marian Reiner.

Page 190: "The Rainbow" by Iain Crichton Smith from *A Scottish Poetry Book*, 1983. Reprinted by permission of Carcanet Press Limited.

Page 190: "Reading" from *Rhymes About Us* by Marchette Chute, published 1974 by E.P. Dutton & Co. Reprinted by permission of Elizabeth Hauser.

Illustrations

PI2-PI7 Mary Anne Lloyd

20-42 Gabriel Pacheco

84-97 Dean MacAdam

108-122 Lin Wang

188-191 Luciana Navarro Powell

Photographs

Every effort has been made to secure permission and provide appropriate credit for photographic material. The publisher deeply regrets any omission and pledges to correct errors called to its attention in subsequent editions.

Unless otherwise acknowledged, all photographs are the property of Scott Foresman, a division of Pearson Education.

Photo locators denoted as follows: Top (T), Center (C), Bottom (B), Left (L), Right (R), Background (Bkgd).

16 ©Stewart Cohen/Index Stock Imagery

17 (C) ©Jose Luis Pelaez, Inc./Corbis, (T) ©Royalty-Free/Corbis

45 Courtesy of Carmen Tafolla

74 (R, L) José Ramirez

75 ©David Jeffrey/Getty Images

76 Getty Images

77 (B) *Education* (2005)/José Ramirez, (TL) *Fruta y Flor* (2007)/José Ramirez, (TR) *Each One, Teach One* (2006)/José Ramirez

80 ©Momatiuk-Eastcott/Corbis

81 (L) ©Richard T. Nowitz/Corbis, (R) ©Jason Horowitz/zefa/Corbis

86 ©David R. Frazier Photolibrary, Inc./Alamy Images

88 ©Medioimages/Jupiter Images

90 ©Glowimages/Getty Images

91 (CR, CL) National Archives

92 ©Private Collection/Peter Newark American Pictures/Bridgeman Art Library

93 Getty Images

94 (Bkgd) ©Skip Brown/National Geographic Image Collection, (TL) ©Jeff Vanuga/Corbis

95 ©Corbis/Jupiter Images

96 Jupiter Images

97 ©Visions of America, LLC/Alamy

100 ©Corbis/Jupiter Images

101 Corbis

104 ©Peter Steiner/Corbis

105 (CR) ©John Henley/Corbis, (T) Jupiter Images, (CL) ©Lindsay Hebberd/Corbis

126 Creatas

127 (T) ©Ariel Skelley/Corbis, (B) ©Paul Barton/Corbis

128 ©Wayne Eastep/Getty Images

132 ©Rob Lewine/Corbis

133 ©Don Mason/Corbis, ©Julie Fisher/zefa/Corbis

157 ©The Ezra Jack Keats Foundation

162 ©Brooklyn Productions/Getty Images

163 (C) Getty Images, (T) ©Patrick Molnar/Getty Images

187 (TR) Photo of Cynthia Rylan t used with permission of Simon & Schuster, Inc./©Margaret Miller

195 Hemera Technologies

196 ©Nik Wheeler/Corbis

197 ©Paul Almasy/Corbis

198 (BL, CR) Hemera Technologies

199 (CL) Hemera Technologies, (BR) ©Amwell/Getty Images

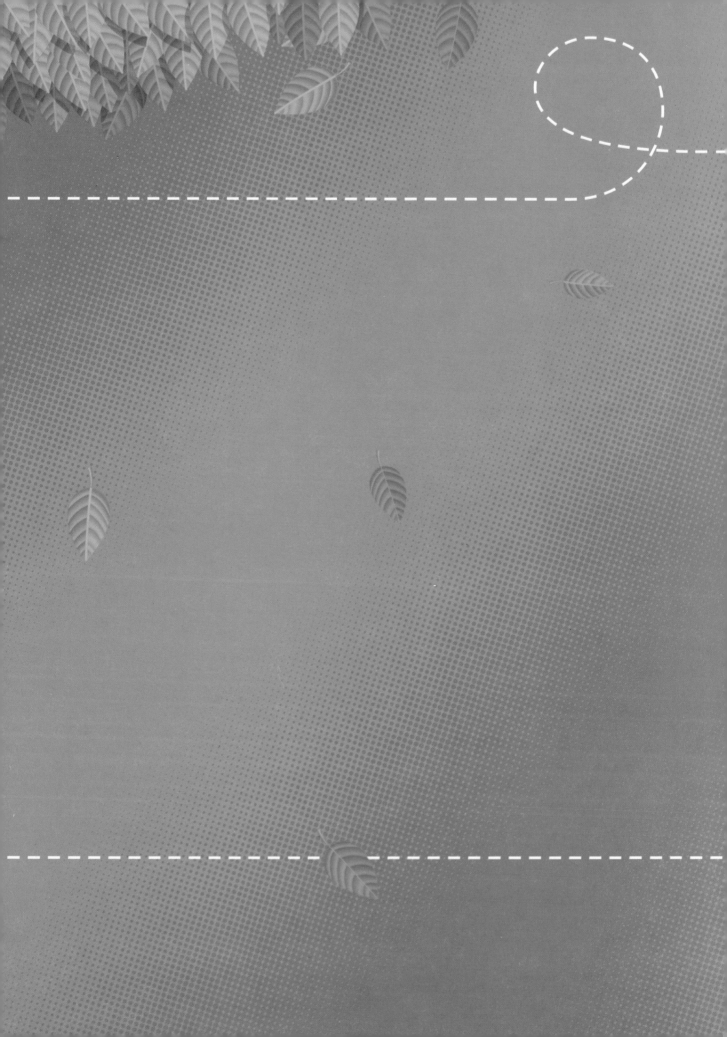